Play Piano with
Abba

CW00420408

Wise Publications
London / New York / Sydney / Paris / Copenhagen / Madrid / Hong Kong / Tokyo

Dancing Queen

Words & Music by Benny Andersson, Stig Anderson & Björn Ulvaeus

You can dance,___ you can jive,_____

where they play__ the right mus - ic   get - ting in __ the swing__   you come to look for a King. __

An - y - bod - y could be that   guy__
You're a teas - er you turn 'em   on__

night is young__ and the mus - ic's   high,   with a bit__ of rock mus - ic
leave 'em burn - ing and then you're   gone,   look - ing out__ for an - oth - er

Mamma Mia

Words & Music by Benny Andersson, Stig Anderson & Björn Ulvaeus

Moderate steady four

1 bar count in:

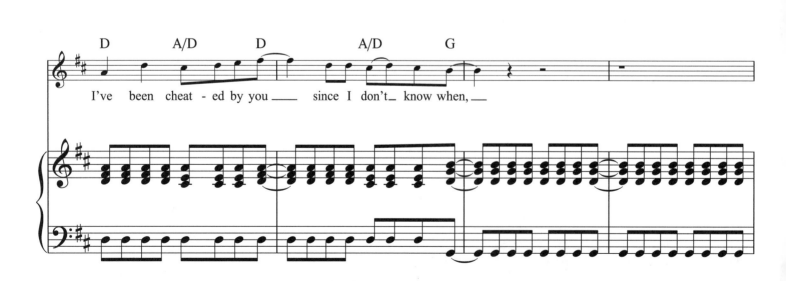

I've been cheat-ed by you ___ since I don't ___ know when, ___

one more look and I for-get ev-ry-thing___ oh,___ oh.___

Mam-ma mi-a here I go a-gain, ___ my, my, how___ ___ can I re-sist you? Mam-ma mi-a does it show a-gain___ my, my, just___ how much I've missed you? Yes,___ I've been bro -

Money, Money, Money

Words & Music by Benny Andersson & Björn Ulvaeus

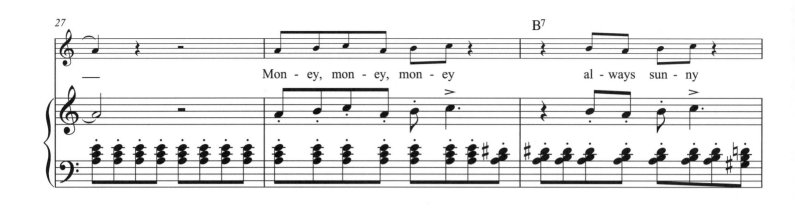

Mon - ey, mon - ey, mon - ey   al - ways sun - ny

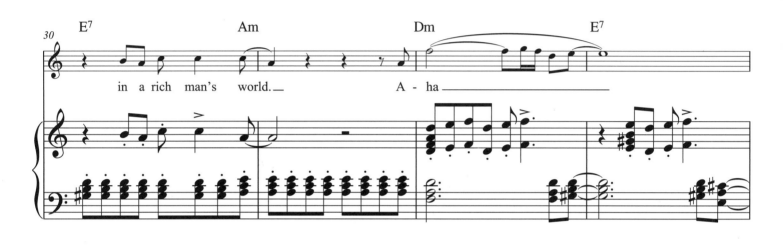

in a rich man's world. ___   A - ha ___

all the things I could do ___   if I had a lit - tle mon - ey,   it's a rich man's world. ___

It's a rich man's world. ___

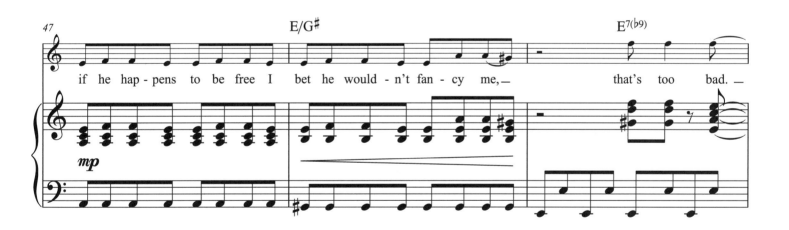

The Winner Takes It All

Words & Music by Benny Andersson & Björn Ulvaeus

I don't wan - na talk a - bout things we've gone through, though it's hurt - ing me, now it's his - to - ry. I've played all my

The gods may throw a dice, their minds as cold as ice, and some - one way down here _____ los - es some - one dear. _____ The win - ner takes it all, the los - er has to fall, it's simp - le and it's plain, _____ why should I com - plain? _____

But tell me does she kiss like I used to kiss you?

Does it feel the same when she calls your name?

Some - where deep in - side, you must know I miss you,

but what can I say, rules must be o - beyed.

Chiquitita

Words & Music by Benny Andersson & Björn Ulvaeus

Chi - qui - ti - ta you and I know

how the heart - aches come and they go and the scars they're leav - ing,

you'll be danc - in' once a - gain and the pain will end you will have no

time for griev - in'. Chi - qui - ti - ta you and I cry

there is no way you can de-ny it, ___

I _____

see that you're oh so sad, so qui - et. ___

D.S al Coda

Chi - qui - ti - ta - you and I ___

CODA

- fore, sing a new song

40

Waterloo

Words & Music by Benny Andersson, Stig Anderson & Björn Ulvaeus

Bright shuffle (swung ♪)

1 bar count in:

11/11 (180568)

CD Track Listing

Full Performance:

1 Dancing Queen
(Andersson/Ulvaeus/Anderson)
Bocu Music Limited

2 Mamma Mia
(Andersson/Ulvaeus/Anderson)
Bocu Music Limited

3 Money, Money, Money
(Andersson/Ulvaeus)
Bocu Music Limited

4 The Winner Takes It All
(Andersson/Ulvaeus)
Bocu Music Limited

5 Chiquitita
(Andersson/Ulvaeus)
Bocu Music Limited

6 Waterloo
(Andersson/Ulvaeus/Anderson)
Bocu Music Limited

Backing tracks only:

7 Dancing Queen

8 Mamma Mia

9 Money, Money, Money

10 The Winner Takes It All

11 Chiquitita

12 Waterloo

MCPS

To remove your CD from the plastic sleeve, lift the
small lip on the right to break the perforated flap.
Replace the disc after use for convenient storage.

Published by
Wise Publications
14-15 Berners Street, London W1T 3LJ, UK.

Exclusive Distributors:
Music Sales Limited
Distribution Centre, Newmarket Road,
Bury St Edmunds, Suffolk IP33 3YB, UK.

Music Sales Pty Limited
20 Resolution Drive,
Caringbah, NSW 2229, Australia.

Order No. AM963314
ISBN: 978-0-7119-8091-4
This book © Copyright 2000 by Wise Publications.
Unauthorised reproduction of any part of this publication by
any means including photocopying is an infringement of copyright.

Compiled by Nick Crispin
Music arranged by Paul Honey
Music processed by Enigma
Photographs courtesy of London Features International

Printed in the the EU.

Your Guarantee of Quality
As publishers, we strive to produce every book
to the highest commercial standards.
The music has been freshly engraved and the
book has been carefully designed to minimise
awkward page turns and to make playing from
it a real pleasure.
Particular care has been given to specifying acid-free,
neutral-sized paper made from pulps which have not
been elemental chlorine bleached.
This pulp is from farmed sustainable forests and was
produced with special regard for the environment.
Throughout, the printing and binding have been
planned to ensure a sturdy, attractive publication
which should give years of enjoyment.
If your copy fails to meet our high standards,
please inform us and we will gladly replace it.
www.musicsales.com